The Mix-up

Learning Simple Sorting

by Lynn Maslen Kertell
pictures by Sue Hendra and John R. Maslen

Scholastic Inc.
New York • Toronto • London • Auckland • Sydney • Mexico City • New Delhi • Hong Kong • Buenos Aires

Sally, Seth, and Tanner wanted
to build a toy village.

"But how?" said Sally,
    looking at the jumbled pile of toys.

Tanner liked toys that rolled.

He wanted to find all the
cars, trucks, and tractors.

Sally was looking for animals.

She found a few.
Where were the others?

Seth wanted to make the buildings.

He needed to find all the blocks.

They found their favorite toys.

They were ready to build!

The trucks, animals, and blocks
made an excellent village!